ANGUS - CU

3 8046

MW00928234

Who Flushed Granny Down the Toilet?

Who Flushed Granny Down the Toilet?

And Other Nutty Nonsense

by

Andrew Collett

Illustrated by Steve Weatherill

The King's England Press
2002

ISBN 1 872438 69 5

Who Flushed Granny Down the Toilet?
is typeset by Moose Manuscripts
in Comic Sans MS 14pt and published by
The King's England Press Ltd,
Cambertown House, Commercial Road, Goldthorpe,
Rotherham, South Yorkshire, S63 9BL

Text © Andrew Collett 2002
Illustrations © Steve Weatherill 2002

All rights reserved. No part of this publication may be
reproduced, copied, stored in any retrieval system, or
circulated in any manner whatsoever without the express
prior written permission of the publisher.

This book is sold subject to the condition that it shall not, by
way of trade or otherwise, be lent, re-sold, hired out or
otherwise circulated without the publisher's prior consent in
any form of binding or cover other than that in which it is
published and without a similar condition including this
condition being imposed on the subsequent purchaser.

The author and illustrator assert their moral right to be
recognised as such under the terms of the Berne Convention
and the Copyright, Designs and Patents Act 1988
(as amended).

Printed and bound in Great Britain by

Woolnough Bookbinding
Irthlingborough
Northamptonshire

Foreword

Thank you to all you nice book-buying people who have managed to empty the nation's bookshelves of over 100,000 copies of my previous revolting rhyme collections. So, no introductions needed. Enjoy!

About the Illustrator

Steve Weatherill is a well-known illustrator and writer who spends most of his time bringing his work to schools and libraries across the nation. Find out more about him at www.babygoz.dabsol.co.uk.

Dedication

To the wonderful children of
St. John the Baptist School,
Spalding, Lincolnshire.

Who Flushed Granny Down the Toilet?

Who flushed Granny down the toilet?
It really isn't fair,
to send her deep-sea diving
without any underwear!

One minute she was smiling,
with both feet on the ground,
when something bit her bottom
and sucked her underground.

But she went down fighting,
she was brave until the end,
waving her walking stick
as she raced round the bend.

She didn't stop to say goodbye,
she didn't wish us well,
leaving us with just a toothy grin
and one terrible toilet smell.

The Day I Blew Up the Dog

The day I blew up the dog
I just wasn't thinking at all;
he didn't deserve to be
blown up with his ball.

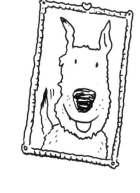

I should have seen his tail
and that puppy face;
instead I watched him explode
and splatter all over the place.

There won't be any more walks,
he'll never curl up in his chair,
for all I've now got left
are four legs and a bit of hair.

He was my very best friend
through times of man and boy,
so it's just as well that my dog
was only a cuddly toy.

Who Puts the Bogies Up Your Nose?

I know why wax grows in your ear
and smells hide in underwear,
I even know why bits of dandruff
jump right off your hair.

I know why armpits smell so bad
and spots grow on your chin,
I even understand
why flies live in the bin.

I know why tissues stick together
and goo grows round your toes,
but one thing I can't understand
is who puts the bogies up your nose?

Are We Nearly There?

Just two minutes into any school journey
and the same words flow through the air:

Please Sir, can you tell us
are we nearly there?

It happens at least twice a minute,
more if the traffic is slow:

Please Sir, can you tell us
how much further to go?

It's the same in every country,
it's famous just about everywhere,
so let's hear it for the first child who cried:

Please Sir, are we nearly there?

Sports Day

On sports day I love
to run in a race,
I love the feeling
of wind in my face.

I love the shouts
of everyone there,
as they all cheer
with hands in the air.

It's just a shame
as I look round to see,
that those shouts and cheers
are never for me!

We Live in a Bed

The family next door
stay in bed all day,
they never get up
to work or play.

All they ever eat
are baked beans and bread,
living together
in a mouldy old bed.

They say it's not bad
living as one,
they love the grime
and terrible pong.

For they never wash
or change their cloth
and use the sheets
to wipe their nose.

But they don't mind,
there's plenty to do,
like collecting bed bu
and eating them too.

So if ever
you've got the time
then visit the family
who live in slime!

Before Toilets Were Invented

Before toilets were invented
we didn't know what to do;
we had to nip outside
if we needed the loo.

Then there were the Romans
who were never shy,
sitting in rows together
to wave as folk past by.

The Tudors filled great potties,
they just thought it fun
to drop them out of windows
and over everyone.

And the great Victorians
really loved to flush,
turning rivers everywhere
into a lovely goo and mush.

But now we've got it right,
we all know what to do,
so everyone let's give thanks
for the modern loo!

The Planet Bog

The Planet Bog
is a place
full of terrible
toilet waste.

Spinning high
above the ground
and flushing
at the speed of sound.

It's like a dark
and big black hole,
pulling planets
down its bowl

Flushing them
to Kingdom Come,
but head-first,
just for fun!

It will eat
you on sight
as its lid
loves to bite.

But do take car
watch its game.
if Planet Bog
pulls its chain.

For what it
really loves to
is to empty
onto me and yo

14

The Big Kiss

Something I hate
and could easily miss
is having my mum
give me a kiss.

I wouldn't mind
if she was discreet,
but one of her kisses
lasts for a week.

It's not a peck,
or even a nip,
but a real lip-smacker
with a vice-like grip.

I have to scream
and swallow for air
as she tugs at my cheeks
and pulls at my hair.

But the worst thing,
what really grates,
is when she kisses me
it's by the school gates.

Which wouldn't be bad,
I wouldn't feel such a fool
if it wasn't always done
in front of the whole school.

The Custard Cannon

The custard cannon
in our school
is fired each day
to feed us all,
filled with special
custard powder
to make its bang
even louder.

With added bits
of spotted dick
thrown in to make
the custard thick,
with chocolate cake
and lemon curd
boiled up gently,
then slowly stirred.

So as the children
walk in slow
the dinner ladies
dip down low,
counting up from
three to four
the custard cannon
starts to roar,

Starts to rumble,
starts to growl,
starts to shake,
starts to howl,
starts to make
the tables rock,
starts to make
our knees all knock.

Then suddenly
there's not a sound,
except of custard
spinning round,
as they wait
for that look
from the special
custard cook

Watching as
she dips a toe
into the cannon,
nice and slow,
then a finger,
just to check,
before jumping in
to her neck

And with a roar
of sudden thunder
she holds her nose
and dips down under,
counting quickly
from three to four
as her head pops up
and down for more.

Bubbling with that
cooking pot
and that custard,
nice and hot.
Until, at last,
with a lick
she starts the cannon
with a kick

Screaming as
it starts to roar,
shooting custard
to the floor,
telling all to
open wide,
to let the custard
drop inside

To stick their tongues
into the air,
to lick the custard
from their hair,
for custard cannons,
when quite hot,
are always such
a rotten shot!

Rock and Roll Around the Toilet Bowl

Let's rock and roll
around the toilet bowl,
let's feel the rhythm
of the toilet seat.

Let's rant and roar
on the bathroom floor
and click our fingers
to the potty beat.

Let's sniff the pong
and break into song;
let's put on
a show.

Let's twist and shout
and splash about,
to make music
down below!

Join the Gang!

Who's going to join my gang?
Who's going to line up first?
I promise you my gang
will be one of the worst!

Who's going to join my gang?
Two more would make it three!
Please someone join my gang,
or I'll just be left with me!

Down the Back of Our Settee

I lost £1
down our settee,
I tried to find it
to set it free,
but all I discovered
was chewing gum,
mouldy cheese,
and one breadcrumb ...

But what was worse,
what made it bad,
were toe-nail clippings
from Grandad,
but nothing could
really prepare
for the boiled sweet
all covered in hair ....

Insects too,
mostly dead,
and earwax from
Grandma's head,
underpants
and a big fat flea
were all I found
down our settee!

But no £1!

Summer Fête Fun

Our head teacher's in the stocks,
he's pretending that it's fun,
and for five minutes at least
there's nowhere he can run!

Which is why we're going to give
everything we've got:
wet sponges, buckets, hose pipes -
he can have the lot!

The only problem is,
our teachers have got there first;
there's no stopping them,
they're out to do their worst!

It doesn't seem quite fair
as we watch him getting wet,
but at least this will be a lesson
our head teacher won't forget!

Dad Wears Curlers

Dad wears curlers
on his head
each night before
he goes to bed.

But not so he
can look all sweet
with curly hair,
nice and neat

But because
he thinks it's cool
to mess about
and play the fool.

But what's worse
is the next day;
at work he gives
the game away.

For he forgets
that they're there
and still has curlers
in his hair.

Maggot Meal

A meal of maggots
isn't very nice,
but who can tell the difference
when they're served with rice?

Our Teacher's Valentine's Card

Our teacher's got a Valentine's card,
he thinks that we don't know,
but we were quick to spot
how his face was all aglow!

He thinks we cannot see
the way he trembles with the chalk,
he thinks we haven't noticed
his funny little walk.

He thinks he's kept it quiet
and we haven't worked it out,
but, on this occasion,
there isn't any doubt!

For what really blew it,
what gave the game away,
is simply that it was our class
who sent it, anyway!

Our Robotic Teacher

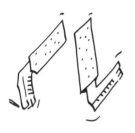

Our robotic teacher,
Mr Chips,
today blew himself
into bits.

His teeth fell out,
his eyes turned pink,
his x-ray vision
went on the blink.

His wires snapped off,
he blew a fuse,
his legs walked off
without his shoes.

The pencil sharpener
on his head
began to spin
and then went dead.

Which is the reason
there's no school,
until we find
the robot tool.

The one to get us
out of this fix
and mend our teacher,
Mr Chips!

When Mum Fell in the Mincer

When Mum fell in the mincer
she tried to scramble out,
she tried to switch it off,
she tried to scream and shout.

But it all happened too quickly,
there was nothing we could do,
except watch as she shot out
in lines of mincemeat stew.

And as we stood and stared
wiping tears from our eyes,
Dad smashed-up the mincemeat
and baked two cottage pies.

"It's what she would have wanted,"
he cried, gobbling them in haste,
"for your mum never liked to see
good food go to waste."

Gladys

I said water the plants, Gladys,
not drown them in one;
I said be quick with the pencils, Gladys,
but that didn't mean to run.

I said push in your chair, Gladys,
not send it flying into the door;
I said keep your homework safe, Gladys,
not lose it deep in your drawer.

I said write in big letters, Gladys,
but that didn't mean on the wall;
I said show us your tap shoes, Gladys,
but instead you danced round the hall.

I said clean-up the paints, Gladys,
but they didn't have to go in the bin;
I say so many things to our class, Gladys,
but with you I really can't win!

And Gladys says ...

Pardon, Miss?

28

Sweaty Betty

Sweaty Betty was never clean
she just dribbled bits of green,
she didn't like to bath or scrub
and never had a wash or rub.

She'd exercise around her yard
so she sweated really hard,
for nothing gave her so much pleasure
as having her clothes all stuck together.

Our Teacher Ate a Cow Pat

When teacher ate a cow pat
there was little we could do
as he quickly licked his lips
and then began to chew.

He munched from the middle,
slurping all the time,
dribbling cow pat on his clothes
with little bits of slime.

He had to have it all,
he had to eat the lot,
for cow pats are best
if gobbled when they're hot.

It was so disgusting,
it really made us cross
that our teacher ate a cow pat
without sharing it with us!

The Parents' Race

Dad is in the parents' race,
he's having lots of fun;
the only problem for our dad
is that he cannot run!

He's spinning round in circles
and waving as he goes,
he's pulling funny faces
and tripping over toes.

They say it's not the winning
it's the taking part,
even though our poor old dad
has barely left the start.

It seems a real pity
that he's no good on his feet,
but when it comes to losing
then Dad's glorious in defeat!

Superstar Dinner Lady

Our dinner lady's a superstar,
she's famous in the town;
she's always on the telly
dancing up and down.

She plays the bass guitar,
has hair down to her knees,
but ties it back on Fridays
when she serves our mushy peas.

She's got a private jet
and a swimming pool:
that's where she makes our custard
before she comes to school.

She plays for Man. United
and scores their every goal,
tackling all the players
with a giant mixing bowl.

Our dinner lady's a superstar,
no one can compare,
unless you've met our caretaker
with his green and yellow hair.

Teacher Riddle

Why is it always the rule
to wave at teachers out of school;
in the supermarket or anywhere
all children love to stop and stare.

It seems most odd indeed
that children have such a need
for they do their best at school next day
to keep well out of teacher's way!

Man and Machine

Dad can't work the vacuum cleaner,
he really doesn't know;
instead of trying to suck things up
he loves to let it blow.

Spiders' legs and dead flies' heads
come flying through the air,
with flaky skin all crisp and thin
and mouldy bits of hair.

Bathroom smells make you unwell
as they're suddenly set free,
rabbit droppings and toilet sloppings
shoot out with mouldy tea!

For when dad gets the vacuum cleaner
he can't help but have a go,
shooting out the gunge and grime
as he switches it to blow!

Grandma's Mouldy Teeth

My grandma's teeth
are very old,
they're all covered
in bits of mould.

Some are black,
some are green,
but they're certainly
never clean.

Some have holes
where beetles and bats
chase around
with tiny rats.

Some have fungus
down each side,
where bugs and slugs
love to hide.

Some have maggots
underneath,
wriggling round
those big black teeth.

We keep away
from grandma's lips
for we know that she
just loves to kiss!

How to Be Bad

If you're out on a school trip
and want to be bad,
if you want to drive
your teachers mad

Don't pull a face,
or cry out loud,
just shout these words
across the crowd:

Sir, I need the toilet, Sir,
Sir, I fear the worst;
if I don't go now, right away,
I think I'm going to burst.

Then watch as he starts to tremble,
watch as he counts to ten,
wait until he gets to eight
then shout those words out again:

Sir, I need the toilet, Sir,
Sir, I fear the worst;
if I don't go now, right away,
I think I'm going to burst.

And as people start to pull back
and children move out of line,
get ready to shout out again
and scream for one very last time:

Sir, I need the toilet, Sir,
Sir, I fear the worst;
if I don't go now, right away,
I think I'm going to burst.

Then wait until everything falls silent,
wait until he spots a loo door,
before smiling and saying politely,
"Sir, I don't want to go anymore!"

Our Dad's Scum

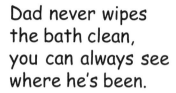

Dad never wipes
the bath clean,
you can always see
where he's been.

It's not great,
it's no fun,
living with
our dad's scum!

It's already
to the roof,
like an iceberg
or rotten tooth.

For after years
of dirty dealing,
our dad's scum
has hit the ceiling.

He doesn't care,
not a bit,
for his scum
is quite a hit

With those people
who don't like soap
and use it as
a dry-ski slope.

And others, who,
as a treat,
think it's really
cool to eat.

But we don't like it,
it's no fun,
living with
our dad's scum.

Germs

Horrible germs
are everywhere,
in your bins
and underwear;
some are big,
some are small,
but the nastiest
ones of all
are not those
when you eat,
or underneath
the toilet seat,
no, the biggest germs
you can't see
are those inside
you and me.

Patty Potts

Poor old Miss
Patty Potts
couldn't stop
growing spots.

She had them
front and back,
she was under
a spot attack.

But it ended
late one night
when she put on
a dress too tight.

Without thinking
she exploded
as her spots
overloaded.

She was gone,
that was it,
squeezed just like a
giant zit.

Never more
to be seen,
except for goo
and bits of green.

41

Hands

We don't wash our hands
when it's time to eat,
for the cheesy bits
make everything sweet.

We let them grow
and turn blue,
we let our fingernails
fill with goo.

It's not that we
don't like waste,
but that these cheesy bits
add extra taste!

Whoops Pyjamas

Our teacher came to school today
not dressed all nice and neat,
but wearing striped pyjamas
and fluffy slippers on her feet.

No one seemed to say a word,
the headmaster didn't shout;
perhaps, today, pyjamas were in
and being nice and neat was out.

But when the day was over
and we lined up at the door,
we couldn't fail to notice
our teacher's quiet snore.

Which must have been the reason,
as he dozed off in his chair,
why, today when coming to school,
he brought his teddy bear!

Letters Going Cheap

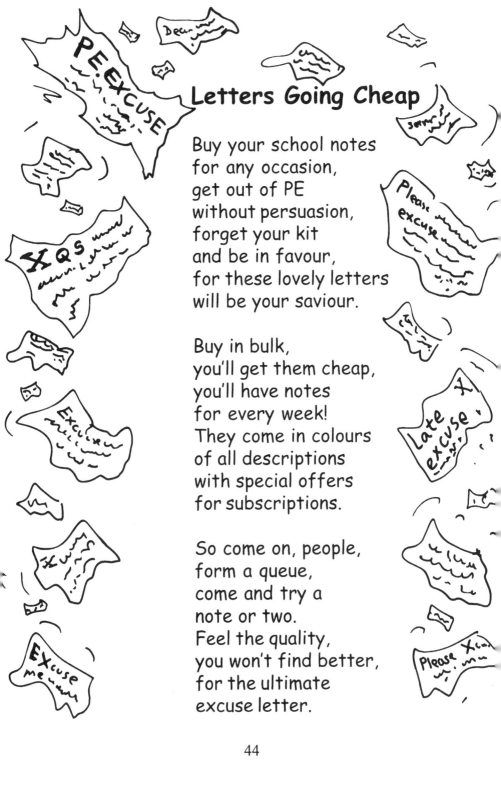

Buy your school notes
for any occasion,
get out of PE
without persuasion,
forget your kit
and be in favour,
for these lovely letters
will be your saviour.

Buy in bulk,
you'll get them cheap,
you'll have notes
for every week!
They come in colours
of all descriptions
with special offers
for subscriptions.

So come on, people,
form a queue,
come and try a
note or two.
Feel the quality,
you won't find better,
for the ultimate
excuse letter.

Toilet Fishing

Dad goes fishing
after dark,
not by the river
or in the park:
it's a strange
thing to do,
but he goes fishing
in the loo.

Just quite why
we don't know,
or what he wants
to find below
but he must
do very well,
judging by
the terrible smell

Of toilet rolls
and other things,
like great big bugs
and worms with wings,
like slimy spiders
all covered in goo
when Dad goes fishing
in the loo.

Teacher's Beard

Our teacher's grown a beard,
it's really quite a sight;
it stretches as wide as us
and is very big in height.

Which might not be amazing,
we just wouldn't mind
if it wasn't that our teacher
was of the female kind!

Sneeze on Toast

We had something for tea today
we'd never had before;
we picked and we licked
as we gobbled it up raw.

But what we didn't know,
what was left unsaid,
was that it wasn't tea at all
but an accident, instead.

We all thought it cheese,
for that's what we like most,
but in one giant cough
Dad had given us ....

... SNEEZE ON TOAST!

My Mum's Smells

My mum's odd,
she's unwell,
for she loves to sniff
any nasty smell.

She likes to play
her grizzly games
by sniffing all the
underground drains.

And sometimes, if
we stop to stare,
she'll be rolling
in old underwear.

But what gives her
a real treat,
are maggots in
mouldy meat,

Beefy bins,
armpit waste,
greasy aprons,
fishy taste,

And even
a dirty nappy
are the smells that keep
MY MUM HAPPY!

Mould

The mould on our wall
had been there for days,
starting to spread
in different ways

With little green legs
and great hairy feet,
until my dad came along
wanting something to eat.

He picked and licked
this mould on the wall,
quickly managing to
gobble it all.

Peeling and pulling
from beneath
with bits still hanging
from his teeth.

He ate it all,
he ate the lot,
for my dad loves mould
when it starts to rot!

What a Save!

Our school goalie saves beer mats
and little bits of chalk;
he saves old rubber bands
and parrots that won't talk.

He saves tiny chocolate mice
and doughnuts with no hole;
it's just a shame our goalie
can't ever save a goal!

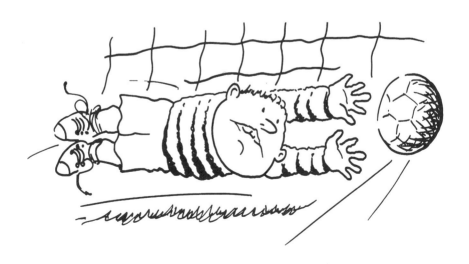

Doggy Loo

The reason all dogs
use a lamppost as a loo
isn't simply
for something to do.

It's because all dogs
just haven't the brain
to lift up the lid
or pull on the chain!

Dad's Two Brains

Our dad is really clever,
he's a scientist you see;
instead of just one brain,
our dad's got three.

The only problem is,
there's no room in his head,
so the extra two
sit on top instead.

You can see them working,
pumping blood and goo,
like two giant jellyfish
beaming back at you.

They pull funny faces
and love to tease the cat,
by dive-bombing his basket
to try and squash him flat.

So do be warned, do take care,
if visiting for the day,
for Dad's two bulging brains
always love to play!

FEELINGS

Feelings
Embarrass and
Enrage, they
Limit and
Inspire, they
Never
Grow old.
So use your feelings, both hot and cold.

Cat on the Loo

When our cat spends a penny
he doesn't know what to do,
for he never runs outside,
but jumps on our loo.

Which might sound funny,
you might think him bright,
as he takes toilet roll
and turns on the light.

But what would be clever,
what would really make us smile,
is if he could also lift the lid
just once in a while.

Mum's Mouth

My mum's mouth is full of worms
living down underneath;
you can see them in a ball
as they wriggle round her teeth.

They like to play silly games
by swinging from her nose;
sometimes playing hide and seek
as they wriggle round her clothes.

And if she should start to shout,
if she should start to bawl,
a great big gooey wormy lump
will splat against the wall.

For my mum's mouth is full of worms,
it's something you'll want to miss,
but spare a thought for us at night
when she gives us a sloppy kiss!

Esmond

(Esmond is my father - a colourful character)

Esmond loved the thrills and spills
of smashing holes in window sills;
he must have been a problem child -
for Esmond really was very wild.

A family argument or other clamour
could send him flying for his hammer
where he would, out of the blue,
demolish a wall or two.

But Saturdays were the danger zone
with Esmond left on his own,
for he'd get rid of everyone
to undo things, just for fun.

Like cupboard doors and roofing tiles,
all watched by neighbours' knowing smiles,
like floorboards and window frames -
for Esmond loved these little games.

But finishing the job wasn't his way,
he'd leave things for another day
for little gave him so much pleasure
as jobs undone, then left forever!

Snog the Bog

When our dad tried
to kiss the loo,
we just didn't know
what we should do.

We had to watch
as he licked his lips
before landing the lid
a sloppy great kiss.

We pulled his arms
and grabbed his feet,
but he wanted a cuddle
with the toilet seat.

"Leave him," cried Mum,
"it's happened before,"
as Dad fell to his knees
and onto the floor.

"It's his new glasses,
he just can't see,
he thinks the toilet's
really me!"

"Darling," Dad shoute
"you make me whole!"
as his head dropped c
the toilet bowl.

"Really?" grinned Mur
in a blush,
before ending it all
with a flush.

Time Flies

My dad dropped a clock
from a window right up high,
to see for himself
if time could really fly!

Nice Day

"Nice day?"
the forty mothers asked
as tiny children
filed out of class.
"Yes, yes, OK,"
they all replied,
except for Jill,
who rarely lied.

But today, inside,
she felt the urge,
a sudden anger,
a particular surge
to tell a whopper,
a little porky,
what fun, she thought,
this being naughty.

And filing out
with thirty nine
she stopped right there,
in her line,
and catching sight
of her mother's eye
she grinned just once,
and began to lie.

"Mummy!" she said,
starting tall,
"my day was not
so nice at all.
I've been a horror,
to say the least,
in fact, I've been
a perfect beast."

Jill stopped, she waited,
she said no more
except to check,
to make quite sure,
that Mummy's smile
was there to stay,
the one which asks,
"Had a nice day?"

"Mother," she continued,
screaming loud
to attract the attention
of the crowd,
"you won't believe
the things I've done
in school today,
to everyone!"

"I found six worms
on Katherine's cousin
then added some more
to make a dozen.
I cut off the pigtails
from old Mrs Murray
then served them up
with the teachers' curry.

"I ran down the corridor
with a scream and a howl,
looking for children
incredibly foul
to taste my hamburgers,
enormous and fat,
flavoured with cobwebs
and odd bits of rat.

"I started at nine,
stopping at three,
busy all day,
as you can probably see;
in fact, I think,
if it has to be said
in a contest for being naughty
I'm a long way ahead."

Jill stopped, she waited,
she said no more,
watching her mum
to make quite sure
that her grin
had clearly gone
to show, today,
that all was wrong.

But no, alas,
to her surprise
as she looked into
her mother's eyes
that great grin
was really there to stay,
the smile which always asks,
"Had a nice day?"

And all the mothers
still standing there,
patting their children,
brushing their hair,
were just the same,
all thirty nine,
those mothers
all smiling in their line.

And so by now
our Jill was done in
with her mother
and that smiling grin;
she had taken no notice,
not one bit;
Jill knew she was beaten -
she had to quit.

And smiling hard
she began to shout
as the same old words
came trotting out:
"I've had a nice day,"
she replied,
Jill, the girl who
sometimes lied.